**Association of Teachers of Mathematics**

# LITTLE PEOPLE

# BIG MATHS

WITHDRAWN

D1581804

A1080480

Published in 2009 by
**Association of Teachers of Mathematics**
Unit 7 Prime Industrial Park,
Shaftesbury Street
Derby DE23 8YB
Telephone 01332 346599
Fax 01332 204357
E-mail: admin@atm.org.uk

Copies may be purchased from the above address or **www.atm.org.uk**

*Printed in England*

# Little People, Big Maths

ISBN - 978 1 898611 61 5

© Jenny Shaw, Emma Howell, Alan Bloomfield

*Jenny Shaw* taught children throughout the primary range for many years before joining the University of Gloucestershire where she specialises in primary mathematics. She still enjoys working with classes of children in local schools, for example in role as chief inspector for giants, and is passionate about using creative activities that involve learners of all ages in talking about mathematics, thinking and problem solving.

*Emma Howell* has spent many years working with little people as a primary school teacher, exploring and developing ideas in which to make maths fun. She has recently joined the University of Gloucestershire to work with bigger people, as a lecturer in the primary maths team.

*Alan Bloomfield* taught mathematics in secondary schools for a long while and in initial teacher training for even longer. Now running his own business, he is still pleased and proud to be an ATM member. Alan acknowledges his good fortune in having had the privilege of working with Bob Vertes, and now with Jenny and Emma in producing the ATM series on People Maths.

### Acknowledgements

We would like to offer our grateful thanks to the following schools who allowed us to try out the activities and take photographs.

Callowell Primary School, Stroud, Glos.

Glenfall Community Primary School, Cheltenham

Lethbridge Primary School, Swindon

We would also like to thank Jackie McNeil, from the university maths team, who tried out some of the activities in school and took photographs for us.

*Mini-whiteboard Bingo is based on an original idea by Ian Sugarman*

# Contents

# Introduction

Why is the book called *Little People, Big Maths*? The first part is very straightforward. The Little People we refer to are those in the Foundation Stage and Key Stage One. The Big Maths needs further consideration as it can be interpreted in a number of ways. In this book 'big' maths can be a reference to the need for the activities to be carried out in a large space, for example, a hall, playground or outside area, or the carpet area of a classroom. Some of the activities contain suggestions for follow-up activities that could be carried out at tables, but the majority involve children moving around and, therefore, needing space to do this.

Big can also refer to size and this is the focus of the activities based around giants in which some activities are used as a basis for exploring measures and creating 'giants'. Another interpretation of the term 'big' maths could refer to the way that the activities involve children working in a large group, for example making human number lines or using circle type activities.

Yet another interpretation could refer to the mathematical ideas suggested within the activities themselves. By presenting the mathematics on a large scale and allowing children to 'see' patterns and sequences of numbers, or by allowing the pupils to physically move around a route or to experience coordinates, more complex or 'bigger' mathematical ideas can be presented to the children. This helps children to make sense of the big ideas of mathematics.

Some of the ideas in this book may be familiar to experienced teachers but we hope that they will provide the basis for generating other ideas and adaptations, both in terms of the mathematics and delivery.

## Resources

The majority of resources needed for the activities are simple to make but they need to be larger than 'normal' classroom ones. For example number cards and shape cards need to be more visible and are therefore more effective if they are A4 size.

Some games require the use of large dice or P.E. equipment, as in *Hoop Groups*. The advice throughout is to 'make it big'.

## Activities

Our aim is to present these in a straightforward manner with a clearly stated focus. This focus could be re-phrased as a learning objective. A list of the resources needed for each activity is included. Most of the games and activities can be adapted for different age groups or mixed age classes and variations are suggested for each of them.

Suggestions for questions to be asked by the teacher are also included. We have endeavoured to suggest questions that promote thinking and develop children's speaking and listening skills. We suggest that teachers consciously build in time during the activities for children to discuss some of the questions with each other or share possible solutions and also have opportunities to explain and justify their answers to the group. This should be viewed by teachers and pupils as a valuable part of the 'big maths' activities. Children should also be encouraged to explore alternative solutions. Question stems such as 'Can you think of another…and another…and another…' can lead to more in-depth thinking.

We have tried and tested all the activities in schools with 'little people'. The photographs in this book are just a sample of our work in school.

# Using the Activities

## Purpose

The activities are designed so that they can be adapted for a variety of different classroom situations. They are suitable for use as stand-alone activities or could form part of a main teaching session. As mental / oral activities, children are able to revise and practise key mathematical concepts and skills. The practical nature of the activities supports kinaesthetic learning, and facilitates discussion and questioning. In addition the activities encourage the development of social skills, spatial awareness, and motor skills. Some of the activities are also well suited to the outdoor environment, such as *Odd and Even Hoops*. The activity *How tall is that Giant?* involves measures and problem solving, but also lends itself to cross-curricular work, such as Art and Design Technology within a fairy tale theme.

The activities are designed to be fun and enable children to develop their mathematical understanding in non-threatening situations. For this reason many involve children working in groups where they can benefit from the support of others. Some of the games and activities are deliberately accessible without complex rules and the need for excessive teacher direction. As a result, children can play many of them independently after an initial introduction. The way that the children subsequently interpret and adapt the games provides further discussion points for enhancing learning.

The activities are appropriate for children within the Foundation Stage and Key Stage One. Suggested variations and extensions provide ideas for differentiating the activities within these age groups.

## Involving everyone

The aim is to involve everyone when planning the activities. This may mean working with the whole class or perhaps rotating the activities around smaller groups. Each activity is designed to encourage participation from all children involved at every stage, whether it is in the manipulation of resources, calculating, asking questions or discussing ideas. In this way children of all abilities can feel involved, be motivated and experience a sense of achievement. Partner work also forms an important part of many activities. This provides support for those less confident allowing them time to discuss their ideas before sharing them with the larger group. The games and activities are generally non-competitive. Competitive elements may be introduced if it suits the learning style of the children involved.

The activities may form part of a main teaching session but they are equally suited to be led by teaching assistants, support staff and parent helpers. Some activities, in particular *How Tall is that Giant?* might be more effective with extra adults to support small groups of children create their paper giants.

The layout of each activity within the book is designed to be accessible to all support staff working with children, parent helpers included. It may be helpful to provide them with an additional sheet giving examples of organisational ideas and further questions that could be asked.

There is no obvious end point for some of the more active games, for example Make a path, and, depending upon the children's response, a decision will be needed on when to draw the activity to a close. All activities can be returned to again and again depending on children's mathematical development and enthusiasm. Repetition of the activities will help young children go beyond thinking about the rules and develop their mathematical thinking in more depth. Variations are suggested at the end of each main activity.

## Organisation

Activities may be organised in a variety of different ways. All activities are active and require sufficient space for children to move around. Several involve one or more children standing at the front of the class and holding cards, for example, *Number Queues*. In these cases it is essential that the rest of the class are able to see both children and cards clearly, hence the need for 'big' resources.

Where the activity involves some kind of game or cards to be placed on the floor so that the children can see, as in *Snakes and Ladders*, it is useful to sit the children in the shape of three sides of a square with the activity in the centre. The teacher can sit along the fourth side so that every child can see clearly. This means that children are seeing the activity from different orientations and it is important to ensure that those children who need to, are seated directly in front of the material.

When working in an outside space we recommend that the area is restricted and children are aware of the boundaries.

## Discussion

A central part to all the activities is discussion. Providing opportunities for children to think out loud and talk about their ideas is a vital part of the learning process. It enables them to test and compare their ideas with others, and brings misconceptions to the teacher's attention. For example in the game *I'm Bigger Than You*, children need to consider the role of zero and how its position affects the value of a number. It is also a valuable opportunity for children to make connections between other areas of learning, both mathematical or other. It is the role of the teacher / leader of the activity to bring these links to children's attention.

Where an activity is repeated independently by children following adult initiation, they should be encouraged to develop their own mathematical talk, share ideas in a less formal environment, and come up with their own adaptations. Appropriate adult interventions can then guide children's talk, and scaffold and develop their ideas further.

Questioning forms a vital part of these discussions. It is important that much of the questioning is open – 'Can you…?', 'Why does that happen?', 'What if…?', 'I wonder why…?'. Such questions could be written onto prompt cards for support staff. Using open questions can avoid putting children on the spot, which can be a threatening situation for less confident children. There will undoubtedly often be times for closed questioning 'How many are there?' 'What is the next number'? Such questioning can help to drive the activity forward and can create vital assessment opportunities.

## Recording

The activities included here do not require children to do any formal recording. However they provide opportunities for children to make their own informal jottings, and for modelling early recording skills. Modelling the recording of the process can support children's learning, and help them make connections between different parts of the problem they are solving.

In some activities a child could take on the role of a scribe for a group, perhaps using a whiteboard to record on, for example to record scores or number sequences.

The activities do also lend themselves as starting points for mathematical learning, which might then lead onto introducing more formal methods of recording later in a teaching session.

An additional member of a staff, a teaching assistant, or parent helper could use these activity times to make observational notes on individual children for the purposes of assessment, either as part of a child's foundation stage profile, or a KS1 teacher assessment. Digital cameras could also be used as a means of recording the children's actions.

# **1** Calculation jigsaw

## **Resources needed**

3 sets of jigsaw cards:
- Set 1 with a number and operation sign
- Set 2 with another number
- Set 3 with an equals sign and the answer to one possible calculation

e.g. $12 + 8 = 20$   $16 - 9 = 7$
    $9 + 8 = 17$   $10 - 4 = 6$
    $9 + 9 = 18$   $20 - 12 = 8$

Note that numbers depend on the age and attainment of the class.

## **Focus**

To fit three cards together to make an addition or subtraction sentence and use up all the cards

## **Task**

The cards are mixed up and placed in the centre of a circle with the children sitting around. Alternatively, use 18 children, each holding one card.

Children should try to fit cards together to make a number sentence. In the set in the example there is a little 'teaser' as children could fit together cards $16 - 8 = 8$ but then would have to re-adjust the number sentences later in order to use up all the cards. Use these kinds of situations as problem solving and discussion exercises.

## **Questions**

What calculation do you want to start with?

Which answer matches the number sentence?

How did you work out the answer?

## **Variations**

Simplify the game by using only addition or only subtraction calculations.

Use multiplication and division calculations.

Use some whole numbers and simple fractions.

Invite children to make up their own set of cards for the class to use. Take care that all the answers are different.

## Resources needed

2 sets of cards numbered 2-12 (They could be different colours and shaped like 'rocks')

2 large 1-6 dice

2 skipping ropes

## Focus

To practise number facts and mental arithmetic

## Task

Using the skipping ropes to represent a river, place a set of 'rock' cards in numerical order on each side of the river. Children are organised into two teams, each sitting behind their 'rocks'. The object of the game is to 'capture' each of the rocks on the other side of the river.

Children take turns to throw both dice and add the spots together. They can then turn over the 'rock' with the corresponding answer across the river.

The first team to capture all the rocks is the winner and is able to 'cross the river'.

## Questions

What numbers do you need to throw on the dice to get the answer 6?

You have thrown a 5 on the first dice, what do you need now to get that 7 'rock'?

Which of the number rocks is easiest to capture? Why?

Which rocks are the hardest to capture? Why?

## Variations

You may wish to use beanbags to cover the rocks rather than turn over the numbers.

Add in 'rocks' with a number 1 and wait for the children to realise that this is not possible with two dice. Discuss how the rule could be altered to make it easier to get a 1 or other 'hard' numbers.

Children can make their own smaller game to play in the classroom.

# **3** Hey diddle diddle, there's a number in the middle

## Resources needed

Small whiteboards and pens

5 cards, each with a 1, 2 or 3-digit number.

Note that numbers depend on the age and attainment of the class but should not be consecutive.

## Focus

To order non-consecutive numbers and then identify other numbers that could be placed in between the original ones

## Task

The cards are shuffled and turned face down.

Five children collect a card and stand in a line in any order. The card should be visible to others in the class who instruct the cardholders to move until the numbers are in the correct order. Another child is then invited to write a number on a whiteboard that is in between two of the existing ones, and then go and stand in the line.

Repeat with other pairs of numbers.

## Questions

Which is the lowest / highest number?

How do you know that this number is higher than this one, e.g. 3 tens rather than 2?

Can you write down a number that would go between these two (original) numbers? And another? And another?

Can you think of a number that would go between these, e.g. 5 and 6?

## Variations

Simplify the game by using regular patterns of odd and even numbers so that there is just one number that fits in the middle.

Increase the range of numbers to include 1-digit, 2-digit and 3-digit numbers.

Use some whole numbers and simple fractions.

Children work in pairs with a set of cards plus some sticky notes and continue the activity during group work.

**Resources needed**

One hoop for each child, spread out in hall or playground

## Focus

To investigate grouping and sharing using the children themselves.

## Task

Children move around between the hoops.

Call out the number '1'. Children find a hoop so there is only one person in each hoop.

Children move again between hoops.

Call out the number '2'. Children find a hoop so there are two people in a hoop.

Continue calling different numbers. Children get into groups in the hoops each time a number is called.

### Odd and Even Hoops

Spread hoops out around the playground, put two bean bags in each hoop. Split people into two teams A and B.

Team A has to ensure that each hoop has an odd number of bean bags. Team B has to ensure that each hoop an even number of bean bags.

Start and stop on the whistle and count the number of beanbags in each hoop.

The winning team is the one with the most odd / even hoops.

## Questions

Is there anyone left over? Why is this?

Is everyone in groups of the right number?

How many hoops are empty / full? What does this tell us?

Can you count in the jumps corresponding to the group size (2's, 3's etc)?

How many hoops are there? There were two beanbags in each hoop so how many bean bags are there?

Do we need any more rules?

Play the game again, this time team A making sure each hoop has two beanbags, and team B, three beanbags?

## Variations

Use as a tidying up activity:

Play once. Ask for all red hoops and their bean bags to be cleared away.

Play again. Ask for all green hoops to be cleared away.

Continue until all hoops are cleared away.

# 5 How long is your foot?

## Resources needed

Balls of string or wool

Tape measures

Rulers

Uniform non-standard measuring equipment e.g. worms

## Focus

To explore generalisations concerning body measurements.

## Task

Introduce the investigation with the question, 'is it true that your foot is about the same size as the distance between your wrist and your elbow?'

Allow the children to discuss this in pairs and try it out. Ask them to choose a piece of measuring equipment to try it out. Does it work for everybody? (This will work exactly for some but not others).

Ask the children to try out other comparisons using their bodies.

e.g. Compare your upper and lower arm sizes – are they the same?

Use this investigation as preparation for the activity How tall is that giant?

## Questions

What apparatus did you choose to measure different parts of your body with? Why?

Which was the most and least effective way of measuring?

What did you find out?

## Variations / extension

- Is it true that your height is the same as the distance between your (outstretched) fingertip to fingertip? (*This is based on an Egyptian term – the stature*)

- Your foot is the same size as the distance between your pelvic bones.

- Hold your thumb against your index finger. The distance between the top of your thumb and top of your index finger is the same size as your nose.

What other comparisons can you make?

## Resources needed

Balls of string or wool

Tape measures

Rolls of kitchen paper

Sticky tape

Template of a 'giant's' foot and hand and/ or a very large shoe or slipper; e.g. size 12 Wellington boots, and a glove or hand template to match

## Focus

To use the generalisations discovered about body measurements to create a 'life-sized' giant.

## Task

This could be part of a theme about fairy tales or giants. Use the information gathered from the activity 'How long is your foot?' The hand and foot might have been 'discovered' overnight, suggesting a visit from a giant. How tall might he be? How could you find out?

Use the information discovered along with the 'giant's' hand and foot to construct a paper giant.

- Draw around hand and foot and cut out the shapes.

- Use these and other body comparisons to construct the arms and body.

e.g. use the information that the length of a foot is approximately equal to the distance between pelvic bones to create the width of the giant's body. Use the stature measurement to create the height.

Children can add features to the giant when the basic body is finished and paint or use collage to complete him / her.

## Questions

Would the giant fit into the classroom or the hall?

How many children are needed altogether to be as tall as the giant?

## Variations / extension

If the children have read the story of Jim and the Beanstalk (Raymond Briggs) they can also consider making hats for the giant or for each other. (The approximate ratio of head circumference to height is 3:1)

Goliath was a giant in the Old Testament. He was 6 cubits and a span tall. Find out what a cubit and a span were and see if Goliath was taller or shorter than your giant.
If you use your own cubit to measure his height, will everyone in the class make him the same height? Test your answer.

Use the **www.guinessbookofrecords** to find out about very tall or small animals and people.

13

# **7** I'm bigger than you!

## Resources needed

6 Chairs in two rows of 3, each set of 3 chairs labelled H, T or U

A set of 10 Cards, numbered 0-9

## Focus

To read, recognise and compare two 3-digit numbers.

## Task

A person from Team 1 selects a card from their team's pack, and chooses a H, T or U chair to sit on, holding the card so it is visible. A person from Team 2 does the same, sitting on a chair in their team's row. Team members continue to pick a card from the remaining ones in their team pack, and seat themselves in their team row.

The winning team is the one which produces the larger 3-digit number after everyone has sat down.

## Questions

What numbers would you put in the hundreds seat to make sure you make the bigger number?

Have you picked a higher or lower number than the one you have already?

What value is this number?

Which numbers are easiest to place? Why?

Why can zero be a difficult number to place? What happens if you pick a zero and only the hundreds 'seat' is left?

## Variations

Simplify the game by using fewer cards or a dice instead of cards.

Make the smallest number to win.

Ask the losing team to rearrange their numbers to see if they can make a larger number? Alternatively allow them to choose 1 more card from the pack and see if they can make a larger number.

Set team challenges, e.g. Who can make a number closest to 200 with their three number cards? Who can make the highest odd number? Who has the highest number when all three digits are added together?

Use arrow cards rather than digit cards. Place these face down so children select one card from each of hundreds, tens and units and then read and compare the numbers. This could also be done as a paired activity.

14

## Resources needed

Sufficient sets of 0-9 digit cards for each child to have one card

## Focus

To make and compare 2-digit and 3-digit numbers.

## Task

Give each child a digit card. Ask a series of questions about the numbers.

Ask the children to get into twos and combine their digits to make a 2-digit number.

Select two pairs to come to the front with their numbers. Ask the class to decide which pair has the higher number and why. What would happen if they reversed the digits in each number?

Ask all the other children to find another pair and arrange their numbers so that they can see which is the higher. At this point it may be easier for them to put their cards on the floor in front of them.

Bring 3 pairs of children to the front with their numbers and order these from lowest to highest. The rest of the children can now move into groups of 3 or 4 and order their numbers.

## Questions

Who has a number more than 4 (40), less than 3 (36) etc?

Who has an odd / even number?

Who has a multiple of 5? Are there any other multiples of 5?

If you had 3 separate digits, what are the highest and lowest numbers you can make?

How can you be sure that this is the highest number? Which is the significant digit?

When there are 3 or more 2-digit numbers on 'display', ask the rest of the children if any pair has a 2-digit number that would be more than the existing highest / lowest number.

Does any pair have a number that would go in between the existing ones?

## Variations

Ask the children to get into groups of 3 to create 3-digit numbers and repeat the activity.

# **9** Make a path

**Resources needed**

Number mats to 20

Dice with sides labelled odd, odd,
even, even, five, five

## Focus

To solve problems using knowledge of
number patterns.

## Task

Put the number mats in a line in any order.
Roll the dice. A child walks along the line
of number mats without stepping on any
mats with the number in that pattern. For
example, if you roll 'odd' you must not step
on any odd numbers. If you roll 5, you must
not step on any numbers in the 5 times table.

You may move along the number line in
steps or jumps, i.e. by stepping from one to
the next, or by jumping over one number.
Step carefully on the mats in case they are
slippery. You may prefer children to step
beside the mats if they are laminated.

Are the numbers in an order that will allow
you to get across all 20 mats?

Repeat laying the mats down once the dice
has been thrown and as the jumps are made,
so finding the best order.

## Questions

What is the best order for the number mats?

Is there only one way of arranging them?

Could you do it if you had to jump over one
each time and not step from one to the next
at all?

## Variations

Simplify by using a dice labelled with odd and
even only.

Increase the difficulty of the calculations by
labelling the dice odd, 2, 3, 4, 5, 10.

Extend the number sequence to 30.

Change to rules so each person must jump
over two numbers on each move.

## Resources needed

16 small whiteboards + pens

2 large dice

16 bean bags (optional)

## Focus

To find two matching cards

## Task

Take turns to throw two dice and ask the children to add the numbers to find the total. Write the total on a whiteboard and put it on the floor. Build up a 4 x 4 array with whiteboards and other numbers made the same way. Children sit around the array. More than one whiteboard may have the same answer but this does not matter.

Once the 16 numbers have been generated, the game can start. Children take turns to throw the two dice, find the total and then look for the answer on one of the whiteboards. If they find the answer they 'mark' the board by covering the answer with a beanbag, turning it over or crossing off the number. Sometimes a total is not represented on the existing array when children throw the dice.

The game continues until all the totals have been found.

## Questions

What is 5 add 6?

What is the total of 5 and 6?

If you throw 5 and then 6 more, how many is that altogether?

Suppose you need to cover the whiteboard with a number 7, what two numbers do you need to throw? Is there another combination?

You have thrown a 4 and need to make 9. What do you need to throw on the second dice?

## Variations

Divide the children into two teams, each with a set of different coloured beanbags or coloured pens to indicate when they have 'covered' an answer. The winning team is the one with the most answers covered.

Use one dice with numbers 7–12 and another with 1–6. Use these to generate subtraction calculations.

Play the same game but multiply the two numbers on the dice together.

Use dice or spinners with larger numbers or more numbers e.g. 0–9.

# 11 Money bags

## Focus

To find the total of the coins, involving the strategy of using the largest denomination first.

## Task

Ask individual children to come and select a coin from the bag.

Initially start with three coins and gradually increase the number of coins as children become more confident.

Tell children that, to help find the total, they need to re-arrange the coins in value order. Move the coins physically putting the larger denomination first and then calculate the total.

Differentiate the game by using different values of coins according to the needs of the children.

## Questions

What coin is this?

Which of these coins is worth the most?

Which are worth more, the copper coins or the silver ones?

This coin is bigger than this one (in size) so is it worth more?

Both teams have a total of 12p but they are not using the same coins. Can anyone explain why the totals are the same?

e.g. 5p 5p 2p and 10p 1p 1p

## Variations

Divide the children into two (or more) teams. They should take turns to collect coins and arrange them. Compare the totals. The team with the higher / highest total earns a point.

This game can be used by the whole class playing in pairs using plastic or real coins and a card strip with 3, 4, or 5 sections.

**Resources needed**

Dice

Coins

Number cards 10 - 50

## Focus

To use addition and subtraction facts to solve problems involving money.

## Task

Children sit in a small group, with coins ranging from 1p to 20p placed in the middle.

Throw a dice. Each child collects the number of coins from the middle corresponding to the number on the dice; e.g. throw a 3, collect 3 coins.

Children add up the total value of their coins.

Who has the most?

Who has the least?

Play the game again, this time try to select the coins that will give you the highest total, again collecting the number of coins corresponding to the number thrown on the dice.

## Challenge

Pick a number from the pile of number cards and place it face up on the table.

Throw the dice to see how many coins each child should collect.

Can you select the coins that will make a total as close to the target number as possible?

## Variations

Each child starts with 20p. The children take turns to throw the dice to find out how much money they must give away. If a child throws a 5, they must subtract 5p from their original 20p, exchanging coins from the pile in the middle as appropriate, to leave them with 15p.

On the next throw, they again subtract the number on the dice, and so on.

Towards the end, children must throw the exact number on the dice to match the amount they have left. For example, if a child has 4p left, and throws a 6, they miss a turn and wait until they throw a 4 or less.

The game ends when one child has given away all of their money.

# **13** Number groups

## Resources needed

A large space e.g. playground, hall

A number label for each child i.e. if there are 30 children have 5 sets of 1-6 labels.

## Focus

To practise simple properties of number.

## Task

Give each child a number label at random before you start the activities. Ask the children to put themselves into groups so that there is one of each of the numbers 1 to 6 in each group or organise the groups more formally.

Children spread around the hall in their groups. Call out instructions such as:

All those with ...

- number 2 wave both hands,
- number 3 stand up and jump 3 times,
- an odd / even number stand up,
- a number more than / less than 4 touch your head.

Gradually call out more challenging instructions such as:

- Sort yourselves out lowest to highest and sit down in a line when you are ready.
- Stand up if you are the 3rd person in your line.
- All the number 3s change to a different group - only one 3 in each group.
- Find a partner in your group so that each pair of numbers makes 7 (6+1, 5+2, 4+3).
- Choose 3 members of the team to put their numbers together making a total of 10.

## Questions

At the end of the lesson use more questions to line the children up e.g.

- All those whose card is the answer to 7−1 line up,
- The answer to 1 more than 4,
- The answer to 2x3 and so on.

## Variations

Use different digit cards e.g. multiples, 2-digit numbers, simple fractions, or coin denominations.

Increase the number of children in each team.

Award points for the first team to complete the task.

Play the game in a circle, asking children to cross the circle or run around the outside when you give a certain instruction.

## Resources needed

A set of 8 cards with number sentences on them giving answers that are consecutive numbers. e.g. 10 + 5 =15, 8 + 8 =16, 2 + 15 = 17.

You might include the answer to the number sentence on the back of the card.

## Focus

To practise number facts and mental arithmetic.

## Task

Give out the cards randomly to children and ask them to stand at the front where others can see. They should hold their cards up so that the number sentences can be seen. The object of the game is to arrange the number sentence cards so that the answers are in numerical order.

Ask questions and allow children to move so that their cards reflect the order. You may wish to turn a card over to reveal the answer once the 'order' has been decided, or to leave this until the end as a means of checking the final result.

When the children think that the line is correct, turn all the cards around to check.

## Questions

Can anyone give an answer to any of those questions? How did you work it out?

Do you think the card will be at the beginning of the line, the middle or the end? Why?

Which number sentence card do you think will have the lowest/highest answer? Why?

What was the answer to this number sentence again, so is the answer to this card going to be a lower or higher number?

## Variations

Use non-consecutive numbers for answers. To extend this game, once the 'final' line has been made, ask children if they could say a number that would fit in between two existing ones and then write a number sentence for it.

Increase the difficulty of the number sentences either through the use of larger numbers or different operations.

Ask children to create their own sets of cards to try out in another session.

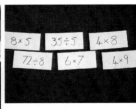

21

# **15** Number picnic

## Resources needed

A set of cards with the numbers 1 – 9 on them so there is one for each child.

A piece of cloth (picnic rug) placed in the middle of a circle of children.

## Focus

To reinforce ideas about the properties of number and use knowledge and reasoning to work out the rules.

## Task

Each child is given a number card. (Differentiate this if necessary).

Initially ask the children some questions and ask them to respond by holding up their card if it fits your instruction.

Hold up your card if it is:

- more than 5
- less than 6
- an even / odd number
- 1 more than …
- 1 less than …
- half / double …

Now decide on a rule e.g. even numbers, but keep this a secret. In turn, children are invited to show their number and ask, 'Please may I come to your picnic? '

If the number fits your secret rule, the child is asked to place it on the rug.

If the number does not fit the rule, the card is placed outside the rug.

After a few turns, ask children to discuss in pairs what the rule might be.

Ask them to explain their reasoning.

Ask a child to decide on a rule and repeat.

## Questions

What does 'more than' mean? How many more than 5 is your card?

Is there another number that is more than 5?

Does anyone think they can guess the rule?

So why do you think that number is not on the picnic rug?

What other numbers could go on the rug?

What others would be outside?

## Variations

Use different numbers.

Use cards with pictures of 2-D shapes.

Use 3-D solids.

22

## Resources needed

A set of cards with ordinal words and symbols on e.g. 1st first, 2nd second etc.

(*This can be played using hats or crowns with number symbols written on them*)

An equal number of cards each with a child's name

A bag or box to put the name cards in

## Focus

To practise using ordinal numbers.

## Task

Spread out the symbol cards where the children can see them. The name cards are shuffled and placed in the bag. Ask a child to pick out a name card from the bag and read it out. The named child selects the card that says 'first' and stands at the front, holding the card. Continue until all the cards are used and there is a line of children.

Read each card and emphasise the language; e.g. This is card number two and so Jenny is second in the line.

Ask questions about the order.

## Questions

Whose name was first out of the bag?

What might it say on the next (order) card?

Who is seventh in the line?

What position is Alan?

Who is between the 4th and 6th people? What position is that?

Who is last in the line?

Who has the red jumper?

## Variations

Use objects e.g. soft toys, cars, instead of children and ask questions about these.

Shuffle the ordinal cards up and ask the children to sort these into a line first and then add objects to the line e.g. put the yellow car first, put the sports car in ninth position.

# **17** Number sentence Bingo

## Resources needed

A set of 10 cards with an addition number sentence on each

A set of A5 cards each with an answer that corresponds to one of the number sentences (Note that each answer should correspond to one question only.)

A bag for the number sentences

## Focus

To practise number facts.

## Task

Ask ten children to select an answer card and stand at the front.

The number sentence cards are shuffled and placed in a bag.

Ask a child from the main body of the class to pick out a number sentence card from the bag and read it out.

Children calculate the answer and the child who is holding the answer sits down.

The game continues until there is only one person standing. S/he can shout 'Bingo' and is the winner.

## Questions

How did you work out that number sentence?

Is there another way?

What number sentence do you think we could have to get an answer 8?

Can you predict who might be the winner?

There are just two answers left – what could the questions be?

## Variations

Use number sentences with subtraction, multiplication and division facts, either just one operation or a mix.

Ask children to make up the number sentences to a given set of answer cards and then try them out in a game.

## Resources needed

A set of 0 - 20 cards

## Focus

To apply knowledge of numbers to make connections and recognise relationships between numbers.

## Task

Children work in pairs. Give each pair three number cards from 0-9. Which one is the odd one out?

**1** **3** **6**

Children make a decision as to which is the odd one out based on a reason of their choice. It may be that one is an odd number and the others are even. One may be made up of straight lines and the others curved.

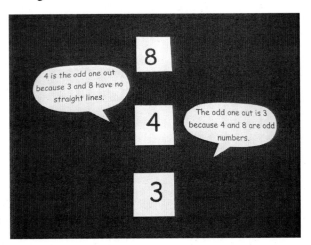

Repeat using number cards 0–20. Encourage children to think of reasons such as 'two of the numbers on the cards are in the five times table and the other number is not'.

## Questions

Can you find three reasons why each card in turn might be the odd one out?

Can you give me two reasons why the same card is the odd one out?

## Variations

Use number cards up to 50 or 100 as an extension.

This game could be played in the same way with shape cards.

# **19** Patterns with numbers

## Resources needed

2 sets of 10 A4 cards each with a single digit between 0 and 9

## Focus

To use the digit cards to create a number pattern and explain this, justifying the choice of numbers.

## Task

Select two number cards and display these for children to see. Explain that this is the start of a pattern and ask which two numbers might come next.

> e.g.  3, 4 … might be followed by:
> 3, 4, 3, 4
> 3, 4, 4, 3
> 3, 4, 5, 6.

As the children become more skilled increase the complexity of the pattern

> e.g.  3 ,5 … which might be followed by:
> 3, 5, 7, 9
> 3, 5, 4, 6
> 3, 5, 8, 12

or add more digits

> e.g.  2, 1, 3, 1, 2  2, 1, 3, 2, 1, 3, 2, 1, 4 …
> 2, 1, 3, 2, 4, 3, 5, 4 …
> 2, 1, 3, 1, 4, 1, 5, 1 …

Encourage the children to think of different variations in the patterns. It might be helpful to record these on the board for children to see and refer to.

## Questions

What numbers could we add to these two to make a pattern?

Is there another pattern we could make?

Could we use the same two (new) numbers to make a different pattern?

Can you explain your pattern?

Can anyone explain the pattern that Peter has made?

What number cards could we use if we wanted to continue the pattern at both ends of the pattern line we have now?

## Variations

Give each child a digit card. Teacher should start the initial pattern by choosing two children (numbers) to start a pattern. Ask the other children if they have a card that they think might continue (or extend) the number sequence. They should come and stand in the line, explaining why they think they could stand in the 'pattern'.

Try the same idea with children holding cards showing 2-D shapes, or holding 3-D solids.

# Patterns with shapes **20**

## Resources needed

A collection of 2-D shapes. Limit the variety so that different repeat patterns can be obtained.

## Focus

To order 2-D shapes into a repeating pattern.

## Task

Ask two children to choose different shapes to come and stand at the front. If you were trying to make a pattern, invite children to suggest what shape might come next?
And next?

Use other children to create the repeat pattern and talk about what it is. Invite the children to verbalise this e.g. circle, square, circle, square.

Repeat with another simple pattern.

Now change the opening pattern e.g. square, square, triangle and ask the children to continue the pattern.

Ask children to offer their suggestions of patterns.

Try the same idea with children holding pictures of simpler objects; e.g. cat, house etc. or more complex pictures; e.g. 3-D solids, numbers.

Could you make a pattern in a circle?

Children could explore patterns using coloured cubes or shapes at their tables.

## Questions

What shape do you think should come next? Why do you think that?

Could you have made a different one?

What shapes could be put next to the original ones so that the pattern continues right to left as well as left to right? (*This will depend which way the children are looking at the pattern*).

How many different patterns can you make starting with 3 shapes?

Do you know any songs that have patterns in them e.g. head, shoulders, knees and toes?

## Variations

Choose one type of equipment – cubes, beads etc. A group of children sit in a circle.

Ask one child to make a pattern with 3 coloured cubes. The next person in the circle adds one more cube to start the pattern repeat. Continue round the circle, each person adding the next cube in the pattern. The pattern chain can be added to at either end.

Choose 6 people from around the circle to start a pattern with 4 cubes, beads on a string or similar. On a signal, pass the pattern chain on to the next person in the circle, they must add the next bead / cube. Continue passing round the circle until the pattern has been repeated 3 or more times.

27

# **21** Question or answer pairs

## Resources needed

2 sets of cards, one set with a number sentence on one side and another set with the corresponding answers; e.g. 4 + 6 on one card and 10 on the other

Note that no two cards should have the same answer in early games but there may be more than one when the children are more familiar with the game.

## Focus

To help children recall number facts.

## Task

Cards are spread face down on the floor, or table, where all children can see them. *Initially it might help children to remember the cards if they are placed in an array rather than randomly.*

The aim of this Pelmanism-type game is to match up all the cards with their answers. Invite one child to turn over a card and say what is on it. Invite another to turn over another card and see if it matches so one card shows a question and the other the corresponding answer.
When a child offers an answer, check by turning over the card. If the answer matches the question, the child places the number sentence where the children can see it, but not in the way of the other cards. If the answer is incorrect, the both cards are turned back over in the middle.
Children are encouraged to remember where particular cards are.

## Questions

Is that a question or an answer?

What is the answer to that question?

How did you work that out? Is there another way of working it out?

What do you think might be the question that would give that answer?

Can you think of another question that might have the same answer? And another, and another ...?

Can you remember where you saw that answer card / question card?

## Variations

Use cards with:

- a number with a corresponding number of dots (domino style)

- a number and the corresponding word card; e.g. 10, ten

- a mixture of addition and / or subtraction questions, multiplication and / or division

- a number symbol to match cards with corresponding vocabulary or image of tens and units

- a fraction symbol to match to an image of that fraction

Have the same answer on 2 or 3 cards but different questions; e.g. answer 12, questions 3 x 4 or 2 x 6 or 1 x 12. Use this as a talking point.

Extend the game by asking children to find three matching cards; e.g. number, number name and image of tens and units

## Resources needed

A set of cards with a number sentence on one side and the corresponding answer on the reverse e.g. 4 + 6 on one side and 10 on the other; e.g. different addition sums with answers up to 20

Note that no two cards should have the same answer in early games but there may be more than one when the children are more familiar with the game.

## Focus

To help children remember number facts and develop ideas about inverse operations and relationships between operations.

## Task

Cards are spread on the floor or table where all children can see them. Have a mixture of number sentences and answers facing up.

Children are invited to talk with partners about any of the number sentences or answers that they see. This encourages some early calculating and predicting.

Children are invited to suggest an answer to one of the cards or a question that might give a particular answer. When a child offers an answer, check by turning over the card. If the answer matches the question, the child receives the card. If the answer is not what is shown, the card is replaced in the middle.

Sometimes a child might give an appropriate suggestion that does not match that on the card. Celebrate and praise the suggestion and use this to discuss alternative answers for the particular number and others.

## Questions

Do you think you know the answers to any of these questions?

How did you work that out? Is there another way of working it out?

Can you think of another question that might have the same answer? And another, and another ... ?

## Variations

Use a mixture of addition and / or subtraction questions.

Use multiplication and / or division.

Have the same answer on 2 or 3 cards but different questions; e.g. the answer 12 could have the questions 3 x 4 or 2 x 6 or 1 x 12. Use this as a talking point.

# **23** Roll a number

## Focus

To practise vocabulary associated with comparing numbers and simple calculations.

## Task

Children should sit in a circle, each having a card (or sticky label) with a number written on it that everyone can see.

Devise a rule; e.g. finding someone with the same digit / number as you.

Roll the ball across the circle to someone with the same number as you. Encourage the children to explain their action e.g. I'm rolling this to Emma because she has a number 4 like me.

Use different rules; for example:

- A number one more than yours
- One less
- Greater than / less than
- A number that, when added to yours, makes 10

Reinforce the vocabulary of the action each time, particularly when you are saying one more or a complement of ten; e.g. I am number 3 and I'm rolling it to Mark who is 7 because 3 and 7 make 10.

## Questions

Is there anyone who has not had the ball yet?

Can anyone think of a question for Michael to ask so that he can send the ball to Mae?

## Variations

Use larger numbers or multiples of 2s, 5s, 10s.

Roll the ball from one person to another then another, then another. Individuals or the whole team could keep a running total and note the score. Repeat the game and compare the totals. Which 3 numbers would enable you to get the highest total?

Create a target number. Roll the ball to different people, keeping a running total, aiming to get to the target number, such as 20. How many numbers were used?

## Resources needed

A set of 1–10 digit cards

## Focus

To use number clues to find a chosen number.

## Task

Give ten children a digit card each and ask them to stand at the front of the class holding their cards so that they can be seen.

Give a series of questions to eliminate one or more numbers at a time. If a number is eliminated, the child holding the corresponding card should sit down away from the group. Each time the class should help with the decision making and discuss in pairs, and then as a group, which children should sit down and why.

Children could be encouraged to make up their own questions by choosing their own 'secret' number and then making some questions to eliminate all but their secret number.

## Questions

Suppose the secret number is 6.

Sit down if your number is:
- More than 9
- Between 1 and 3
- One more than 6
- Double 4
- More than 3 but less than 6
- Half of 2
- Bigger than 7
- Next to 4
- And the secret number is...

## Variations

Use larger numbers and / or more cards.

Devise more open questions using terms such as more than, less than, between, etc.

# **25** Shape match

## Resources needed

A 2-D shape for each child

Use a selection of regular and irregular shapes of different sizes and, if using pictures of shapes, use different orientations. This will avoid giving the idea that all triangles are equilateral or a square rotated 45 degrees is a diamond rather than still a square.

## Focus

To become more familiar with the names and properties of 2-D shapes by matching shapes with similar properties.

## Task

Children sit or stand in a circle holding their shapes so that others can see them. Begin by asking various 'show me' questions to reinforce names and properties.

Then play the game by asking children with shapes that match your instruction to hold up their cards or swap places. You may decide to give clear instructions here for the children to go around the outside edge of the circle to do this or swap across the middle.

Other commands could include swapping all those shapes with:

- straight sides
- more than 3 sides
- 4 corners
- right angles
- that are rectangles

Ask children to think of commands themselves.

## Questions

Show me a 3-sided shape?

What is it called?

How is your triangle the same as Lucy's?

What is different?

Is it still a triangle if I turn it upside down? Why?

## Variations

Try the same idea with children holding 3-D solids.

Adapt the game by using numbers.

**Resources needed**

A set of cards with consecutive numbers e.g. 0–20

Various sized ladders and snakes made of card

A large (floor) dice

A large space in which to play

Children could sit around the three sides of a square with the cards in the middle so that they can all see and take turns in playing the game.

## Focus

To order numbers from 0–20 and then practise counting on or back.

## Task

Hand out the number cards randomly initially. Ask children to come and place the cards on the floor in order, making 4 rows of 5 in a shape that resembles a snakes and ladders board

| | | | | |
|----|----|----|----|----|
| 20 | 19 | 18 | 17 | 16 |
| 11 | 12 | 13 | 14 | 15 |
| 10 | 9 | 8 | 7 | 6 |
| 1 | 2 | 3 | 4 | 5 |

Select two children to become 'counters'. (*They will need to be able to move **alongside** the card numbers rather than step on them for safety reasons*). Ask others to place the snakes and ladders on the board. Working logically around the 'square' of children, ask one child to throw the dice and say the number, ask the next child to 'move the counters' counting out loud as s / he does so.

Establish rules, if necessary, such as needing an exact throw of the dice to finish etc.

## Questions

Where shall we place the snake – what would happen if we put it on number 20?

How many more does David need to get to the ladder?

What will we need to throw on the dice so that Peter does not get on the snake?

How many did Suzie go back when she went down the snake?

## Variations

Use more numbers.

Start at 20 and work back to zero.

Use two dice and add these together to get the total number to move.

Ask the children to make penalty cards (e.g. move on 2, move back 3) rather than snakes and ladders and let them decide where to place these.

Encourage children to design their own board games and rules (based on a track) to play in the classroom.

# **27** Snowman sort

## Resources needed

Pictures of snowmen painted by the children.

When painting these, ask children to make them the size of the sheet of paper and give their snowmen features e.g. hat, scarf, buttons, broom etc.

## Focus

To find different ways of sorting a set of snowmen pictures.

## Task

Select 10 snowmen and attach them to the board so that the children can see them.

Find different ways of sorting the snowmen into two groups. Ask the children to physically come and move the snowmen into the different sets and explain their ideas.

Use hoops or a paper frame to sort the snowmen into these. Ask questions about the finished diagrams.

Encourage children to think about the different attributes of the snowmen as they sort them e.g. a set of snowmen with blue scarves and a set of snowmen who do not have blue scarves.

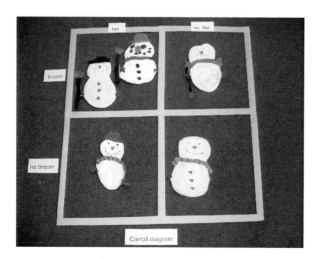

## Questions

What do you notice about the snowmen?

Is there anything the same about any of them?

Is there anything the same about their hats? How many red ones are there?

Can you sort the snowmen into two sets? What is in each set?

Why can't this snowman go into this set?

## Variations

Use 4 pieces of sugar paper to make a Carroll diagram. Ask the children to decide upon criteria and sort the snowmen;

e.g.

|  | blue scarves | not blue scarves |
|---|---|---|
| hats |  |  |
| not hats |  |  |

Try the same idea with different pictures; e.g. houses.

34

**Resources needed**

4x4 grid

Beanbags of different colours

## Focus

To solve a simple problem using practical equipment.

## Task

Prepare a large 4x4 grid that can be placed in the middle of the group, on the carpet or on the table. Introduce and discuss the vocabulary: horizontal, vertical, diagonal.

### Two colours

Ask children to fill the squares using just beanbags of two different colours, so that beanbags of the same colour are not touching either horizontally or vertically. Discuss what they need to do to make it possible.

### Three colours

Introduce a third colour and repeat the activity.

Is it possible to arrange the beanbags now so that like colours are not touching?

Can they arrange the beanbags without them touching vertically, horizontally or diagonally?

## Extension: Four colours

Suppose you have 4 colours?

Is it possible to arrange the beanbags now so that like colours are not touching?

Can you think of different ways?

Record the different ways in which you could fill the grid with 4 colours.

Encourage children to predict how many ways there might be if there were 5 colours.

Children could explore this in pairs using small grids and coloured counters.

## Variations

This game could also be played with numbers or shapes instead of colours.

35

# **29** Target number

**Resources needed**

Sets of 20 cards, numbered 1–20

## Focus

To add numbers to a given total, and find the difference between two numbers.

## Task

Share out the cards, one per child. Call out a number, for example, 21.

Children move around and get into groups so that their numbers add up to 21.

Compare groupings.

Who is left out? What numbers do they need?

Repeat with other target numbers.

Children pair up and compare number cards to find the difference between their numbers.

Each pair then tries to find a third person to join their group. The third person has the card with the difference number on it.

## Questions

Is it possible for everyone to form a group?

Are any particular numbers always left over?

Can zero be included as one of the number cards?

## Variations

In the hall, spread out the 1–20 number cards to form a large grid or number line. Give each child a card. Children move into pairs. Each pair then works out the difference between their two numbers and sits on the matching number on the large grid / number line on the floor.

If a pair finds their number has already been taken, they must seek out new partners to make a difference number that is still unoccupied. The game finishes when no more groups can be made.

Does the game finish every time?

Which numbers will always be unoccupied?

Try again using the numbers 1–30.

## Resources needed

Large pictures of 2-D shapes and / or 3-D solids displayed on white board / interactive whiteboard

Alternatively use a hat with a shape on it

## Focus

To describe and know the properties of 2-D shapes and 3-D solids.

## Task

Choose a child to stand at the front with their back to the board. Display or reveal a picture of a shape. The rest of the group offer hints about the properties of that shape to help the child guess what it might be.

When the child works out what the shape is, choose a different child to have a turn.

Continue changing the shape on display for each new child.

Introduce an element of competition.

## Questions

Can children work out the shape with only 3 clues?

Can the group help the child at the front guess the shape correctly in less than 10 seconds?

## Variations

Divide the class into two teams. Prepare a sequence of ten shape pictures on the interactive whiteboard. One member from each team stands at the front with their back to the board. Team members call out clues to help the child work out what shape is behind them. Time how long it takes for the team to get through all the shapes.

Repeat with the second team, using a different sequence of ten shapes prepared on the interactive white board. Which team scored the fastest time?

Alternatively, a time limit of one minute could be set and the goal is for each team to help the child at the front work out the most shapes. This would require advance preparation of a larger set of shapes.

This game could also be played with numbers or mathematical symbols, instead of shapes.

# **31** What's the link?

## Focus

To know and use number bonds to 20.

## Task

Give each child one digit card.

One child stands up and says a calculation to which their number is the answer.

Children then take turns to join the line, saying the addition or subtraction calculation to link their number to the previous person's. For example:

- 1st child
  My card says 5.
  I know that $2 + 3 = 5$

- 2nd child
  My card says 14.
  I know that 5 add 9 makes 14.

- 3rd child
  My card says 8.
  I know that $14 - 6$ makes 8.

Rule – Children cannot join the chain with the next consecutive number.

Continue until all cards are used.

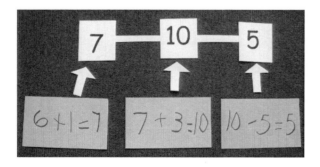

## Questions

Can you think of a calculation to link the last card to the first to form a loop?

Can you now repeat the activity going the other way round the group?

Can anyone think of a calculation for their number that uses multiplication or division?

Can you link your number without using a calculation? (Formed with straight lines, a 2-digit number, starts with the same letter, they are the ages of my sister and brother, they are both in the 5 times table, etc).

## Variations

Simplify by using digits 0–10. Introduce the rule that you must use a different function to the previous person i.e. if one child creates a link using addition, the next person must use subtract, multiply or divide.

Extend by using multiplication or division calculations, and individual whiteboards in the place of the cards.

Children use their 2x, 5x, or 10x table facts to choose a number that links to the previous one, writing each on a white board;
e.g. $10 \times 3 = 30$, $30 \div 5 = 6$, $6 \times 2 = 12$.

Addition and Subtraction can only be used once a chain has become 'stuck'.

## Resources needed

16 cards, each with a number on one side (initially single digit)

A mini whiteboard and pen for each team

4 labels A, B, C, D

4 labels 1, 2, 3, 4

## Focus

To develop skills in using simple coordinates.

## Task

Cards are shuffled and placed face down in a 4x4 array. Label the columns with the alphabet card and the rows with the number cards.

Divide the class into two teams. Ask the children how they might describe the exact position of the cards, encouraging the use of the horizontal axis first and then the vertical e.g. D3.

Teams take it in turns to give a coordinate and turn over the appropriate card. The card is left in place with the digit visible and one team member records their number on the whiteboard. This is repeated until all the numbers are exposed.

Teams should keep a running total of their numbers. The winning team is the one with the highest total.

## Questions

How can you explain the exact position of this card?

Team A has a total of 27 and team B has 22. What numbers do team B need to turn over to be sure that they will have the higher total after their turn?

## Variations

Change the condition for the winner e.g. lowest total, nearest to a target number.

Use a mix of single and 2-digit numbers.

Use some whole numbers and simple fractions.

Use other units e.g. periods of time such as 15 minutes, 1 hour, ½ hour.

Use amount of money or pictures of coins.

# **33** Who goes where?

## Resources needed

A set of 10 A4 cards numbered 1–10

A set of 10 A4 cards with simple fractions on e.g. ½, ¼, 1½, 1¾ etc.

10 plastic wallets

## Focus

To order a set of fraction cards from smallest to largest.

## Task

The cards should be prepared by inserting a number card and fraction card into each wallet. The smallest fraction card should go with card number 1, next lowest with card 2 and so on.

The cards are mixed up and given to 10 children who stand in a line at the front holding their cards with the fraction side visible to the rest of the class.

The rest of the class should instruct the cardholders to move around so that the cards are then placed in order from smallest to largest.

Ask the cardholders to turn their cards around as a means of checking. If the fraction order is correct then the number cards on the reverse should also be in the correct sequence.

## Questions

Which do you think is the smallest / largest of those fractions?

Can you draw a picture or diagram to show what that fraction might look like?

How do you know that one is smaller / larger?

Can you think of a fraction that could go next in the line? And another, and another ...?

## Variations

Increase the range of fractions to include higher mixed fractions.

Children could invent their own fraction lines for other children to use. These could be recorded on new cards.